Violin Exam Pieces

ABRSM Grade 5

Selected from the 2012–2015 syllabus

Name

Date of exam

CD

Violin & Piano

Piano only

Contents

Violin consultant: Philippa Bunting
Footnotes: Edward Huws Jones (EHJ), Richard Jones (RJ) and Anthony Burton

Other pieces for Grade 5

First published in 2011 by ABRSM (Publishing) Ltd, a wholly owned subsidiary of ABRSM, 24 Portland Place, London W1B 1LU, United Kingdom
© 2011 by The Associated Board of the Royal Schools of Music

Music origination by Andrew Jones
Cover by Økvik Design
Printed in England by Halstan & Co. Ltd, Amersham, Bucks

MIX
Paper from responsible sources
FSC™ C109619

Corrente

Second movement from Sonata in D minor, Op. 5 No. 7

Edited by and continuo realized by
Richard Jones

Arcangelo Corelli

The Italian composer Arcangelo Corelli (1653–1713) studied in Bologna as a young man, and in the 1670s moved to Rome, where he achieved great fame as a violinist, composer, teacher and orchestral director. In the 18th century, his sonatas and concertos were revered as models owing to the classical purity of their style.

This corrente (literally, 'running' movement – the Italian version of the French courante) is taken from the celebrated set of 12 Violin Sonatas, Op. 5, which Corelli dedicated to the Electress Sophie Charlotte of Brandenburg in 1700. They became the most influential violin sonatas of the 18th century: Charles Burney remarked, in his *A General History of Music* of 1789, that these were the sonatas 'on which all good schools for the violin have since been founded'. RJ

Source: *Sonate a violino e violone o cimbalo*, Op. 5 (Rome, 1700)

A:2

Allegro

Fourth movement from Sonata in A, HWV 361, Op. 1 No. 3

Edited by and continuo realized by
Richard Jones

G. F. Handel

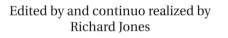

During the years 1724–6, when George Frideric Handel (1685–1759) was firmly established as an opera composer in London, he composed nine sonatas, including three for violin and continuo. It is thought that their composition might have been linked to his post as music master to Princess Anne and Princess Caroline, daughters of the future King George II. One of these works is the Violin Sonata in A (HWV 361), whose finale is reproduced here. It is a characteristically tuneful and sprightly dance movement in the rhythm of a gigue. Handel borrowed it from his Recorder Sonata in B flat (HWV 377), transposing and revising it in the process. The dynamics are editorial suggestions and may be varied. RJ
Source: autograph MS, Cambridge, Fitzwilliam Museum, MU MS 261

A:3

Andante

First movement from Sonata in F, TWV 41:F4

Edited by and continuo realized by
Richard Jones

G. P. Telemann

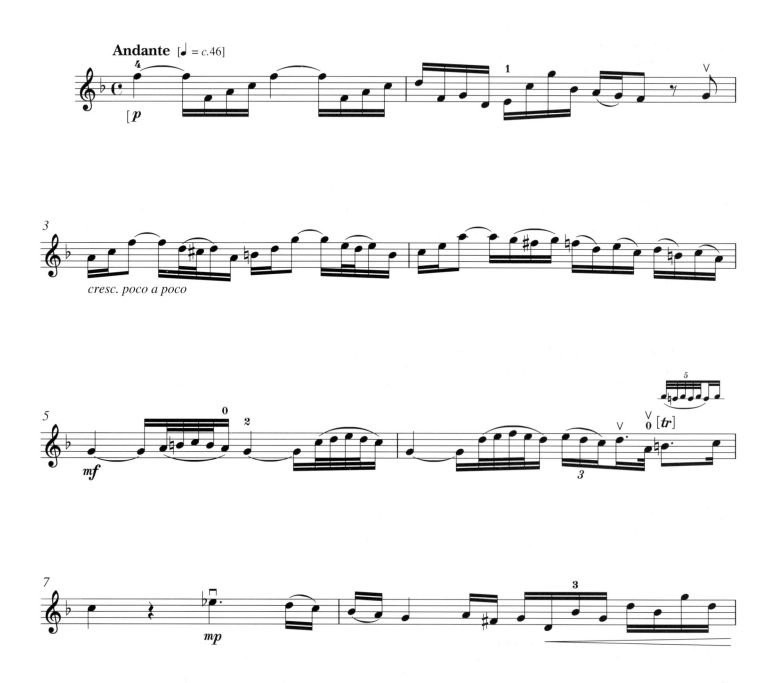

Georg Philipp Telemann (1681–1767), one of the most prolific and versatile composers of his day, studied at Leipzig University and held court appointments at Sorau (now Žary, in Poland) and Eisenach before becoming city music director at Frankfurt (1712) and then at Hamburg (1721).

The Sonata in F for violin and continuo, which opens with this Andante, is the first item in *Essercizii musici* (published in 1740, but probably composed in the 1720s), which comprises 12 solo sonatas and 12 trio sonatas. The Andante consists of a florid, eloquent *cantabile* melody in three sections (ABA') – the first cadencing in the dominant key at bars 6–7; the second (from the middle of bar 7) moving through two minor keys; and the third (from bar 13), a varied repeat of the first, remaining in the tonic key. In the original edition, the 7th violin note of bar 10 reads *c'''*, not *d'''*, in error. The dynamics are editorial suggestions and may be varied. RJ

Source: *Essercizii musici* (Hamburg, 1740); exemplar in Staatsbibliothek zu Berlin – Preußischer Kulturbesitz, Musikabteilung mit Mendelssohn-Archiv

Gavotte

Violin part edited by Mary Cohen

Adam Carse

Adam Carse (1878–1958) was born in Newcastle upon Tyne, and studied in Germany and at the Royal Academy of Music in London, where he later taught harmony and counterpoint. He composed some orchestral music early in his career, but he is better known for his numerous pieces of educational music for school orchestras and solo performers. He was also a collector of old wind instruments, and wrote the authoritative studies *The Orchestra in the 18th Century* and *The Orchestra from Beethoven to Berlioz*. This piece, first published in 1921, is in the 18th-century dance form of the gavotte, in lively tempo and beginning on the half-bar; the minor-key trio section begins as a musette, that is over a bass drone imitating that of the musette or small bagpipe.

© Copyright 1921, 1994 Stainer & Bell Ltd, 23 Gruneisen Road, London N3 1DZ www.stainer.co.uk
From *Classic Carse*, Book 2. Used by permission. All enquiries about this piece, apart from those directly relating to the exams, should be addressed to Stainer & Bell Ltd, 23 Gruneisen Road, London N3 1DZ.

9

(*last time* **rall.**)

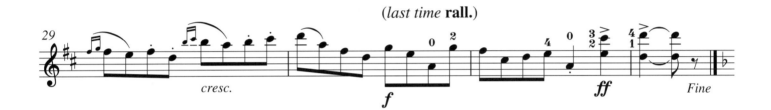

AB 3584

B:2

Pastorale

Op. 23 No. 1

Oskar Rieding

Oskar Rieding (1840–1918) was born in north Germany, studied in Berlin and Leipzig, and worked as an orchestral violinist in Vienna. But he spent most of his career in the Hungarian capital, Budapest, where he was leader of the Opera orchestra from 1871 to 1904. After that, he retired to Cilli (Celje), then in Hungary but now in Slovenia. Rieding wrote many educational works for violin with piano. Some of the best known are in the form of concertos or concertinos, but there are also sets of shorter pieces. One set begins with this melodious *Pastorale*, in a key traditionally associated (for example in Beethoven's Pastoral Symphony) with the countryside.
Source: *Pastorale*, Op. 23 No. 1 (London: Bosworth, 1905)

Tempo I

B:3

Petit air varié

No. 7 from *Petite école de la mélodie*, Op. 123, Book 2

Edited by Richard Jones

Charles Dancla

Petit air varié Little Air with Variation; **Petit école de la mélodie** Little School of Melody

Charles Dancla (1817–1907) was a French violinist, teacher and composer, who studied at the Paris Conservatoire (1828–40), where he taught the violin from 1855, becoming professor in 1860. He played in Paris orchestras, as a soloist, and in concerts of chamber music, partly with members of his own family. He also wrote 14 string quartets, violin methods, and many studies and other educational pieces.

In bar 14, *ou bien en bas* ('or else below') means that, as an alternative, the two violin *d"*s could be played an octave lower on stopped and/or open strings. In the variation, dotted rhythms are best assimilated to triplets, so that ♫ = ♪³♪. RJ

The direction *marcato e punta arco* (accented and at the point of the bow) in bar 65 is optional for exam purposes.

Source: *Petite école de la mélodie. 12 petites pièces pour le violon avec accomp¹. de piano*, Op. 123 (Paris, 1868)

Variation

Moderato e cantabile [♩ = c.104]

For Latin Lovers

Brian Chapple

Brian Chapple (born 1945) studied at the Royal Academy of Music in his native London, and has since combined composing with piano playing and teaching, most recently in Devon. Although he wrote several orchestral works in the early part of his career, he has concentrated since then on composing for choral societies and cathedral and church choirs. But he has also written music for young performers, including this piece, first published in 1998. It is in the rhythm and the gently parodied style of the Latin-American tango, a dance which probably originated in Cuba in the mid-19th century but is most closely associated with Argentina.

AB 3584

Slow and Fast

Edited by Gabriella Lenkei

Pál Kadosa

Pál Kadosa (1903–83) was one of the leading Hungarian musicians of his generation, a composer of orchestral, vocal and instrumental music, a pianist who gave many first performances, and a teacher of both composition and piano at the Budapest Academy of Music. His *Lassú és Friss*, included in a Hungarian anthology of *Music for Violin* published in 1973, is named after the two main sections of the traditional Hungarian *Verbunkos*, or 'recruiting dance', respectively 'Slow and Fast' – an outline which was also adopted by Liszt in his *Hungarian Rhapsodies* for piano or orchestra. The piece uses semitone dissonances to almost percussive effect, echoing the music of Kadosa's great Hungarian predecessor Béla Bartók.

© Copyright 1973 by Editio Musica Budapest
All enquiries about this piece, apart from those directly relating to the exams, should be addressed to Editio Musica Budapest, H-1132 Budapest, Victor Hugo u. 11–15, Hungary.

C:3

Kozanis

Arranged by Edward Huws Jones

Trad. Greek

This tune is named after the city of Kozani in northern Greece. The 7/8 metre (3+2+2) makes for some exciting rhythms and these need to be played incisively around the middle of the bow and quite near the bridge. The double stops use the open strings as drones, first the A string and later the E string; practise these passages first as a single line, with just the moving part. In this arrangement the performance gains an extra edge by modulating upwards – and by getting faster – for each repetition of the melody. EHJ

Even faster